The Christmas Story

For Sophie and Friends

First published in Great Britain in 1989 by
PAVILION BOOKS LIMITED
196 Shaftesbury Avenue, London WC2H 8JL
in association with Michael Joseph Limited
27 Wrights Lane, Kensington, London W8 5TZ

Illustrations © Copyright Isabelle Brent 1989

Extracts from the Authorized King James Version of the Bible
which is Crown Copyright in England are reproduced by
permission of Eyre and Spottiswoode, Her Majesty's Printers, London
The words are taken from
Luke 1:5, 26, 27, 30–33, 38; 2:1, 3–5, 7–16, 18–20, 40;
Matthew 2:1–3, 8, 9, 11–14, 19–21, 23

Designed by Tom Sawyer

A CIP catalogue record for this book
is available from the British Library

ISBN 1-85145-366-0

10 9 8 7 6 5 4 3 2 1

Printed and bound in Great Britain by
MacLehose & Partners Ltd.

With thanks to Colin Webb and Maria Leach, my editor,
for all their help and encouragement.

THE CHRISTMAS STORY

from The King James Version

Illuminated by
·ISABELLE·BRENT·

PAVILION
MICHAEL JOSEPH

IN THE DAYS of Herod the King, the angel Gabriel was sent from God unto a city named Nazareth, to a virgin espoused to a man whose name was Joseph; and the virgin's name was Mary.

And the angel said, Thou shalt bring forth a son, and shalt call his name Jesus. He shall be called the Son of the Highest: and of his kingdom there shall be no end.

And Mary said, Behold the handmaid of the Lord. And the angel departed from her.

IT CAME to pass that there went out a decree that all the world should be taxed, every one in his own city. And Joseph went up from Nazareth to the city called Bethlehem, to be taxed with Mary his wife, being great with child.

AND SHE brought forth her firstborn son, and wrapped him in swaddling clothes, and laid him in a manger; because there was no room for them in the inn.

There were in the same country shepherds keeping watch over their flock by night. And the angel of the Lord came upon them, and they were sore afraid.

AND THE angel said unto them, Fear not: for behold, I bring you good tidings of great joy. For unto you is born a Saviour, which is Christ the Lord. And this shall be a sign unto you; ye shall find the babe wrapped in swaddling clothes, lying in a manger.

Suddenly there was a multitude of the heavenly host saying, Glory to God in the highest, and on earth peace, good will toward men.

The shepherds said one to another, Let us now go to Bethlehem. And they found Mary and Joseph, and the babe lying in a manger.

And all they that heard it wondered at those things which were told them by the shepherds. But Mary kept all these things, and pondered them in her heart.

And the shepherds returned, praising God.

BEHOLD, there came wise men from the east, saying, Where is he that is born King of the Jews? For we have seen his star in the east, and are come to worship him.

WHEN HEROD the King heard these things, he was troubled. And he sent them to Bethlehem, and said, Go and search diligently for the child; and when ye have found him, bring me word again, that I may come and worship him also.

When they had heard the King, they departed; and lo, the star went before them, till it stood over where the young child was.

And they saw the young child with Mary his mother, and fell down and worshipped him; and when they had opened their treasures, they presented unto him gifts: gold, and frankincense, and myrrh.

Being warned in a dream that they should not return to Herod, they departed into their own country another way.

AND THE angel appeared to Joseph in a dream, saying, Arise, and take the child and his mother, and flee into Egypt, for Herod will seek the child to destroy him.

When he arose, he took the child and his mother by night, and departed into Egypt, and was there until the death of Herod.

BUT WHEN Herod was dead, an angel appeared in a dream to Joseph in Egypt, saying, Take the child and his mother, and go into the land of Israel: for they are dead which sought the young child's life.

And he took the child and his mother, and came into the land of Israel, and dwelt in Nazareth.

AND THE
child grew, and waxed
strong in spirit, filled with
wisdom: and the grace of God
was upon him.